Story texts based on scripts written by Carol Noble, Bridget Hurst and Olly Smith

Illustrations from the TV animation produced by Tiger Aspect

PUFFIN BOOKS
Published by the Penguin Group: London, New York, Australia, Canada,
India, Ireland, New Zealand and South Africa
Penguin Books Ltd, Registered Offices: 80 Strand, London WC2R 0RL, England

puffinbooks.com

First published 2008
Text and illustrations © Lauren Child/Tiger Aspect Productions Ltd, 2005, 2006, 2007, 2008
The Charlie and Lola logo is a trademark of Lauren Child
Made and printed in Italy

ISBN: 978-0-141-38403-0

characters created by
lauren child

My
extremely good
Charlie and Lola
ANNUAL 2009

This ANNUAL belongs to:

PUFFIN

Contents

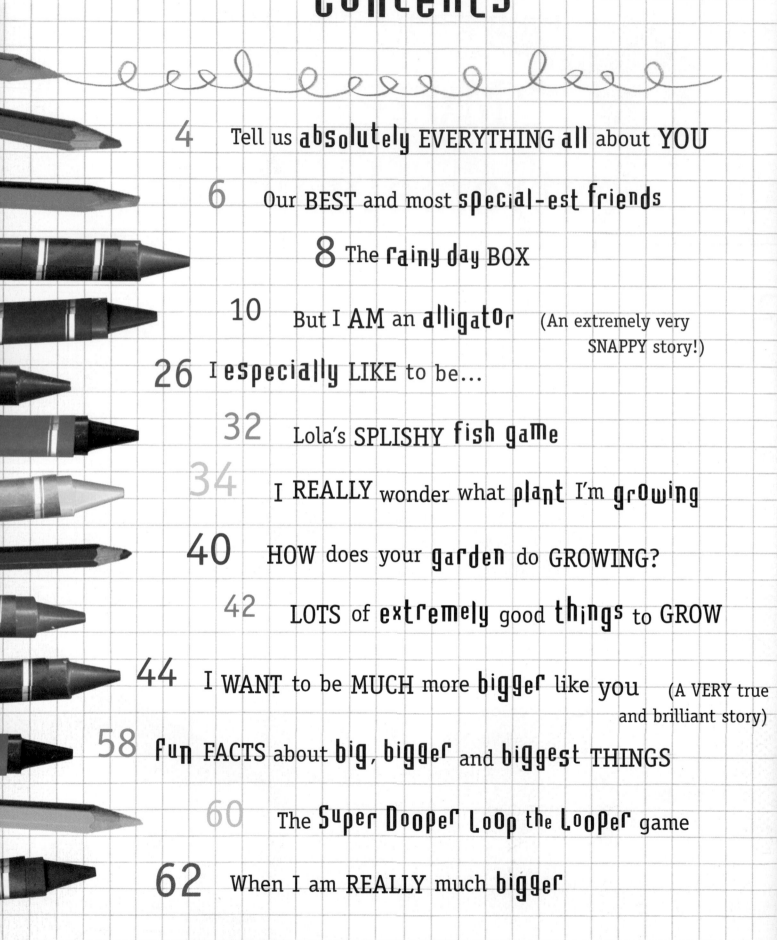

I have this little sister Lola.
            She is small and very funny.
She is very good at playing games
            and finding especially fun things to do...
even when it is raining.

Tell us **absolutely** EVERYLY all about **YOU**

My **name** is:

ERIN

_____

I am __5__ years

and ____ **months** old.

Here is a **picture** of me!

Lola says,
"Yellow is my very
most **favourite** colour,
and I really do love **drawing**…
and **dancing**…
and drinking **pink milk**."

Write a list of your favourite things.

BEN 10
HIGH SCHOOL
MUSICAL 12E
SURF KIDS
WALL@
BEE MOVIE

Lola **especially** likes playing with her big brother, Charlie.

Draw some of your favourite and BEST people here.

CALFUM & LAYFE

Tame's

Lola and Charlie live in a high-upish **flat** in a BIG block.

Draw your **house** or flat or wherever YOU live here.

5

Our BEST and most special-est friends

Lola and I have some extremely very good FRIENDS.

My best friend is Marv.
Marv lives in our block
of **flats** and has one BIG
brother, Marty, and one
littler brother, Morten.

Marv likes
music and
football and
his sausage
dog, Sizzles!

Lola's best friend is Lotta! They like **reading** and **painting**, and they play lots of imaginary **games** together... like their **farm**, which has chickens and pigs and... a GIRAFFE.

Lola's imaginary friend is Soren Lorensen. No one else can see him except for Lola. She shares all her **secrets** with Soren Lorensen because he is an especially good LISTENER.

ALL about MY **friends**

My **best friend** is:

Eosn

Draw a picture of your **best friend** HERE.

Some **things** we like doing together are...

Pl

The rainy day BOX

Lola does absolutely NOT like it when it is pouring with **rain** and she has to stay **indoors**...

But then we make up a special **rainy day** box and have a **rain race**.

You have to think of lots of very good games to play **indoors**. Then you have to try and finish every game... before the rain **stops**!

You can keep all the things you need for the **rain race** in a very special **rainy day** BOX.

Here are some EXTREMELY very good games that you could do for your **rain race**...

Noughts and crosses

Draw a **grid** using four straight lines like the one in the picture. Two people play, and one person **draws** noughts, the other **draws** crosses. Players take it in turns until one person has **drawn** either three noughts or three crosses in a row and wins the game.

Tiddlywinks

Divide up all your tiddlywinks so each player has all the tiddlywinks in one **colour**. Place a pot or plastic cup in the middle of all the players.

Each player uses a **squidger** (a bigger tiddlywink) to press down on one side of each of their smaller tiddlywinks to make them **jump up** into the air.

Players take it in turns to do this and eventually get their tiddlywinks into the **pot**. The first player to get all of their tiddlywinks into the **pot** is the winner!

The tray game

Ask a grown-up or biggish person to arrange TEN **things** on a tray and cover it up with a tea towel or cloth. All the players sit round the tray and have a very quickish look at the **objects**.

When everyone is ready, the cloth is put back over the tray and the players have exactly ONE minute to **remember** what all the **things** on the tray are.

The person who **remembers** the most items correctly is the winner. The winner then has to make up a very good **story** all about the items on the tray!

9

But I AM an alligator

(An extremely very
SNAPPY story!)

I have this little sister Lola.
She is small and very funny.
Lola really loves her alligator costume.
I say,
"Why do you like alligators
so much, Lola?"

"Because alligators are very funny,
and did you know all-i-gators live in swamps and rivers
where they are very difficult to see?

That's because they are
ca-moo-flarged.

And you know,

alligators lay eggs,

not babies.

"And sometimes
   they grow

BIGGER than even our table!" says Lola.

"So you see, Charlie, alligators
are really very interesting.
That's why I am going to wear
my alligator costume
ALL the time."

So I say,
"ALL the time, Lola?"

At the park,
Lola is STILL wearing her
alligator costume.

Marv says,
"Have you asked
her to take it off?"

"A **gazillion**, million times,
but she says
she is going to
wear it FOREVER!"

And Marv says,
"Well, she can't wear
it to **school**, can she?"

And I say,
"NO! She **can't** wear it
to **school**!"

"Of course
I am going to wear it
to **school**," says Lola.

And I say,
"I really don't think it's such a good idea.
    Won't your friends think wearing an **alligator costume**
        is a bit **strange?**"

Lola says,
    "No, Charlie. I think they will all want
alligator costumes too. Especially when I do my **talk**."

So I say,
 "YOUR TALK?"

And Lola says,
 "Yes, Charlie! We have to do a talk
in assembly tomorrow. It's called
 'All About Me'."

Then I say,
 "But you are NOT an **alligator**, Lola.
Don't you think it would be better
 if you tell the whole school
 about YOU, dressed as YOU?

 Maybe you could tell
 them about...

"...how you like

drawing...

...and how you

always hop into bed...

18

...and how pink milk is your favourite and your BEST."

Lola says,
    "That would not be very interesting.
    Everybody already knows I like pink milk!"

And so I say,
    "I could help you with your talk,
        if you like."

But Lola says,
"I do not need any help."

At assembly the next day,
Lola says,
"My name is Lola,
and I like
dressing up.

At the moment,
I like **dressing** up as
an **all-i-gator**
because it is my most
favourite costume
and it is my best."

"I used to like **dressing** up as...

a Spanish lady!

But I could also **dress** up as...

Or sometimes as a circus person.

22

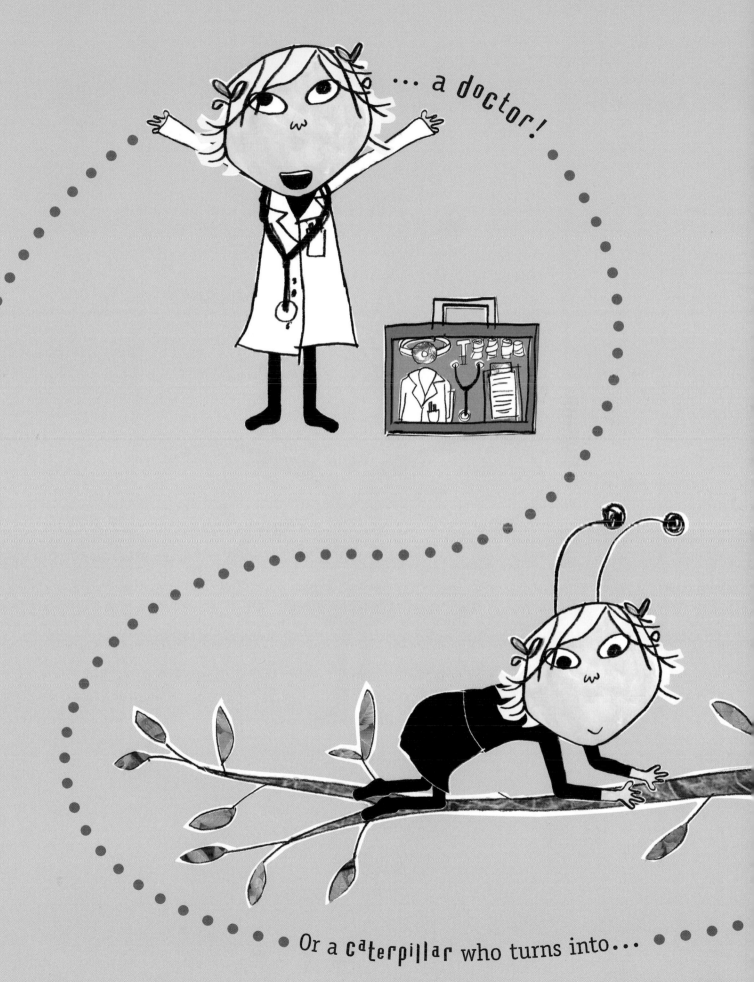

... a doctor!

Or a caterpillar who turns into...

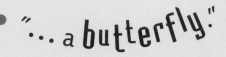

"...a butterfly."

And the
whole school says,
"Wow!"

Lola says,
"I love **dressing** up, because I can be whatever
I want to be... and that is my **best**."

Everyone cheers.
And I say, "Well done, Lola!"

The next day,
Lola is not an **alligator**.
She has whiskers, pointy ears and a tail.

Lola says, "Meow!"

And I say,
"Oh no."

I especially LIKE to be...

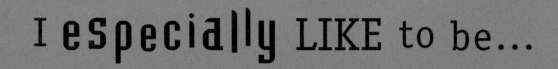

Charlie and Lola and their friends are **dressing up** for their school assembly.

Follow the **instructions** below to make your own very special Charlie and Lola **paper cut-outs**.

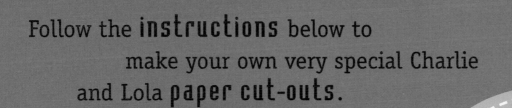

You will need:

- Safety scissors
- Some glue
- Some card (an old cereal box will do)
- A grown-up to help

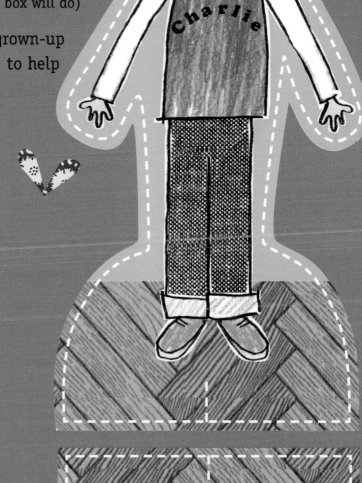

① Carefully cut out the next two pages from this book.

② Stick Charlie and Lola on to some card and cut them out.

③ Now cut out Charlie and Lola's favourite costumes.

④ Fold over the tabs on either side of the costume to make your paper person complete.

29

Help them to get **dressed up**
and talk about their
favourite outfits!

Lola's SPLISHY
fish game

You will need:

Some strong paper or card

A cardboard box

Safety scissors
(and a grown-up to help)

Crayons, paint or felt-tip pens

Some paper clips or split pins

A few long sticks, pencils
or chopsticks

Lots of string

Some magnets
(fridge magnets will do)

Glue or sticky tape

1 First decorate your cardboard box to make it into a **fishpond**. If you don't have a box, you can make your own using some pieces of card.

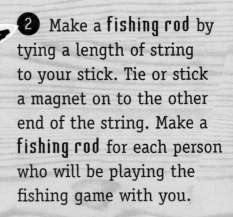

2 Make a **fishing rod** by tying a length of string to your stick. Tie or stick a magnet on to the other end of the string. Make a **fishing rod** for each person who will be playing the fishing game with you.

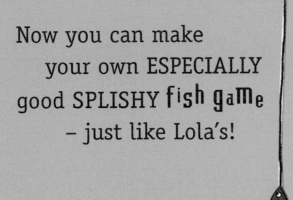

Now you can make your own ESPECIALLY good SPLISHY fish game – just like Lola's!

3 Draw some **fish** on to card or paper or use your special stickers, and then cut them out. Stick a paper clip or split pin on to the noses of each of your **fish**, and throw them in the **fishpond**!

When all the **fish** are gone, count how many each person has caught. The person with the most **fish** is the winner!

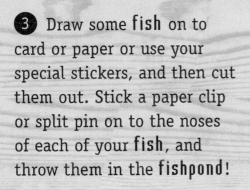

4 Now you're ready to play. Each person picks up a **fishing rod** and uses it to "catch" as many **fish** as they can! The magnet will make the **fish** stick to the **fishing rod**.

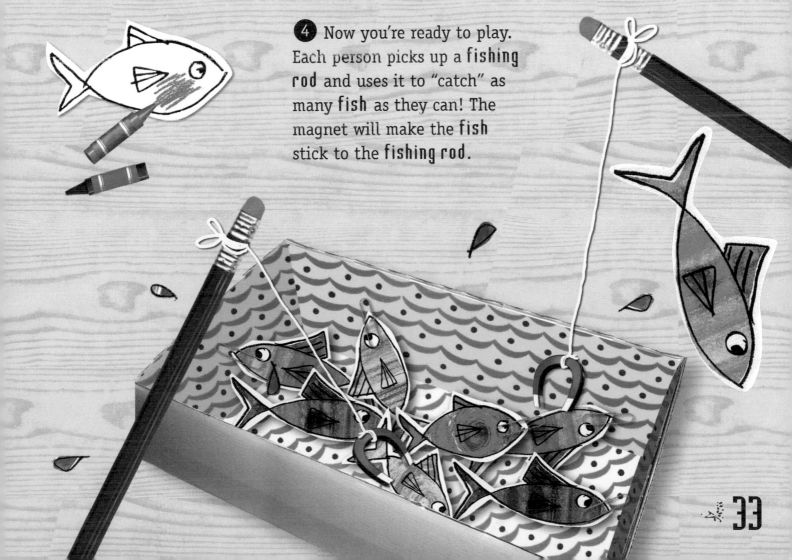

I REALLY wonder what plant I'm growing

I have this little sister Lola.
She is small and very funny.
At the moment I am **growing**
a **tomato** plant.

"I think I'd like to **grow** a plant too," says Lola.
"But I am NOT keen
on **tomatoes**."

So I say,
"That's OK. You can **grow**
any sort of plant you want."

Lola says, "I can grow...

a **biscuit** plant!

A **music** plant!

Or a **butterfly** plant!"

But I say,
"Well, not exactly **any**
kind of plant."

Charlie

Then Mum buys Lola
a pack of **seeds**.
"What do I do now, Charlie?" asks Lola.

I say,
"You put one **seed** in the soil, then cover it up.
And if you take care of it, it will **grow**."

Lola asks, "What will my **seed grow** into, Charlie?"

And I say,
"I don't know.
We'll just have to wait and see."

Then I say,
"Lola, **seeds** only **grow**
when they're **happy**.
And the first thing
they need to be happy is **water**.

Their **squiggly** roots
drink up
the **water** when it rains.
That makes the
plant grow."

Then Lola asks,
"What **else** will make
my plant **happy**, Charlie?"

And I say,
"**Sunshine**. It makes all the
leaves come out."

Lola says, "Charlie, I really **wonder** what plant I'm **growing**...

maybe it will be a **pineapple** plant...

or maybe one of those **prickly** plants.

Or maybe a

huge
t**a**ll
tree!"

A few days later, Lola says,
"It's a flower, Charlie!
And it has a smell.
I have grown a smelling flower.

And it is
extremely special."

HOW does your **garden** do GROWING?

Lola and Lotta are doing some extremely good **gardening**.

Use the stickers on your sticker sheet to help them **grow** some especially good **plants**.

What is **growing** in that **big pot**?

What is Lotta watering with her special **watering can**?

Add some more **beetles**, **bugs** and **butterflies**!

LOTS of extremely good things to GROW

You can grow some COMPLETELY **very** good things
– just like Lola!

Cress

1 Fill a pot with some kitchen roll or cotton wool, then use some water to make it nicely damp.

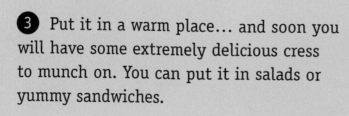

2 Sprinkle some cress seeds into your pot.

3 Put it in a warm place... and soon you will have some extremely delicious cress to munch on. You can put it in salads or yummy sandwiches.

Ever-so-sunny sunflowers

1 Fill some clean, dry empty yoghurt pots with compost.

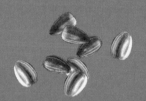

2 Plant a sunflower seed 12mm deep in each pot and cover with some plastic wrap to keep them warm!

3 When some leaves start to appear you can take the plastic wrap off, and once the plants are a tiny bit bigger you can ask a grown-up to help you plant them into a bigger pot, or even plant them outside in the garden.

4 Don't forget to water your sunflowers and make sure they get plenty of sunshine.

5 You will also need to be very extremely patient because it sometimes takes sixty days for the seeds to turn into flowers!

43

I WANT to be MUCH more bigger like you

(A VERY true and brilliant story)

I have this little sister Lola.
She is small and very funny.
Lola says, "I'm not small, Charlie.
I am getting more **bigger**
and grown-up all of the time."

"And now that I am much more bigger, I can go on the Super Dooper Loopy Loopy ride."

"Aaaagghh!"

So I say,
"The **Super Dooper Loop** the **Looper** is very, very SCARY. Are you sure?"

"I am **very** sure, Charlie," says Lola.

So I measure Lola
to see if she really is
bigger.

"Charlie, I must be
more **taller** than that!
Are you **tricking** me?"

"No, Lola.
That's EXACTLY
how **big**
you are."

Then Lola says,
"But I absolutely
MUST be **big** enough
to go on the
Super Dooper
Loopy Loopy ride."

I say, "There are still
loads of **fun rides**
at the fair for
smaller people.
The **Chug-a-Bugs**
ride is **really exciting**."

And Lola says,
"I **don't** think so, Charlie."

Then Lola says,
"I have a GOOD plan.
I am going to
think myself **bigger**.

Now I am thinking I am nearly as **big** as a sunflower touching the sun...

"And now I am
thinking I am as
big
as one of those
EXTREMELY

T
A
L
L
E
S
T

buildings."

I say,
"You can't MAKE yourself **bigger**, Lola.
It just happens."

"But it's not fair, Charlie.
Why am I always, always
the small one?"

So I say,
"There are great
things about
being small.

"You get **stories** read
to you every night...

and you get loads of
piggybacks."

But Lola says,
"I still really, **really**
would like being
the **biggest.**"

When Marv comes over,
he says,
"Are you ready for
the **Super Dooper**
Loop the **Looper**?"

And Lola shouts,

"I am!
I am!
I am!"

Then Marv whispers,
"She's quite **small** for the ride,
isn't she, Charlie?"

And I say,
"Yup."

At the fair, Marv says,
"The **Super Dooper**
Loop the **Looper**
is going to be the BEST ride!"

"Yes.
It will make our hair
stand on **end**," I say.

But Lola's not so sure...

When we get to the front of the line,
    Marv says, "**Hold on** to your tummy, Lola!"

But Lola says, "Err... I think I might be
    slightly too small still.

Perhaps it would be a
    little more **fun** if I went
on something for more
    slightly **smaller** people...
    like the **chug-a-Bugs**!"

So we all go on the **Chug-a-Bugs**
and Lola **laughs** and **laughs**.
          She says, "You were right, Charlie!
The **Chug-a-Bugs** IS the very best ride
          in the whole world and the universe."

fun FACTS about big, bigger and biggest THINGS

Did you know that the **tallest** animal in the world is a **giraffe**? They can grow up to 5.5 metres tall.

The River Nile is an EXTREMELY long river – it travels through ten countries in Africa!

Did you know that the **polar bear** is the **biggest** kind of bear?

"Look, Charlie!

I can maybe

be as tall

as a

giraffe

too!"

"I'm sure

I can travel

THAT far!"

"I did know that, Charlie,
but when I grow up I will
be much,
much
bigger!"

Fill in your own
biggest and best
FACTS!

The **tallest** person I know is

_____

who is _____ metres tall.

The **smallest** person I know is

_____

who is _____ metres small.

My height is _____ metres
and I am extremely BIG.

The **biggest** thing
I have ever seen is

_____

and it is _____ metres high!

1 START HERE
2
3
Do 10 star jumps
5
6
7 Zoom forwards another five squares
8
9
10
11
12 Stand on one leg and count to 10
13
14
15
16
17
29
30
31
32
33
34
35 Oh dear! You have to miss a go
36
37
38
39
40
42
43
44
4

The Super Dooper Loop the Looper game

Now you can play the especially good **Super Dooper Loop the Looper** game!

Use your **favourite** colouring pencils to decorate your game. You can make some **counters** using the stickers at the back of this book – just stick them on to some card and cut them out.

How to play:

Choose a **counter** and put it down on the start square. Each player rolls the **dice** and moves their counter the number of spaces shown. If you land on a square with a **forfeit** you have to do the task – no cheating! Whoever gets to the end first is the **winner**.

You can make up your own tasks or choose extra ones from the sticker sheet and pick which squares to put them on!

Board squares:

28

27 — Oh dear! You've got to go back to 24

26

25

Sing a nursery rhyme

23

22

21 — Hop round the room backwards

20

19

If you talk before your next go, move back 4

46

48

49

THE END You've won! 50

18

When I am REALLY much bigger

Lola is small and very funny
but she is also EXTREMELY excited
about getting **bigger**.

Lola says
"When I am **bigger**, I will be
allowed to go on BIG bike rides just
like you and Marv, Charlie.
I will be able to look after
Sizzles ALL by myself.
And I will be EXTREMELY
very **tall**, Charlie –
even **taller** than you!"

Some of the **things** I will
be able to do when I am **bigger** are...

Lola says
"When I grow up I would like to be...
an actual **doctor**! And have a
stethoscope, and make
people feel **better**."

Lotta says,
"When I grow up I would like
to be a **princess**!
Wouldn't you like to be
an actual **princess** too, Lola?"

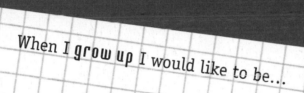

When I **grow up** I would like to be...

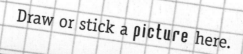

Draw or stick a **picture** here.

"Look, Lola!" I say. "It's sunny outside now.
Shall we go to the park?"

And Lola says, "But there are LOTS of fun
and good things to do INDOORS, Charlie...
Maybe we should play just one more
rainy day game first?"

Use these stickers for **Lola's splishy fish game** on pages 32–33

Use these stickers for the **super dooper loop the looper** game on pages 60–61

e these stickers for **how does your garden do growing** on pages 40–41